HELLO

The purpose of this journal is to provide a much-needed fixed point of reflection, prayer, gratitude, and worship. While these things are not reserved for the Sabbath only, that consecrated day may hold the key to a *thriving faith*. In a world drenched in confusion, worry, and every shade of turmoil, God knew we would desperately need a Seventh Day. **A day of divine rest, renewal, and connection.**

I used to think the Sabbath was going to serve *me*. But I'm learning the truth is that *I* was made to serve the Sabbath. This journal has become more than a place to jot notes each Sunday—it has become a personal record of the goodness of God in my life, a pillar of the worship and truth I've found in quiet moments carefully set aside each week.

—Courtney Casper

FINDING

Sabbath

JOURNAL BREAKDOWN

Finding Sabbath *has a specific layout and design to help you*

◦**Find a higher perspective**
◦**Uncover your divine purpose**
◦**Reflect on what you're learning with God**
◦**Vulnerably process and offer gratitude**

FIND

This section can be used each week to focus and center your Sabbath day worship. It begins with an area titled *"Today's gratitude,"* where you can gently reflect on the good you've seen that week, as well as sections of both lined and white space to offer notes and inspiration, and a gray area where you can sum the week up based on what you *learned, studied,* and *read.*

GRATITUDE

This section is dedicated to simply remembering, recording, and focusing on the GOOD! the JOY! I believe what we look for, we *will* find. Looking for, recognizing, and focusing on our gratitude precedes abundance and peace.

REFLECT

This section can be used to guide your heart in reflection and praise as you process your thoughts with God. Putting these things down on paper often bridges the gap between repetitive spiritual practices and vulnerable connection with Heaven.

I feel/I know
Sometimes, the sneaky lies of the adversary seem like truth. Breaking down how you're feeling versus the TRUTHS that you KNOW can shine light into the darkness, start the healing process for even small wounds, and break down walls of insecurity in our prayers.

Check in
Reflecting on what you're learning about God and how it changes the way you live day to day is a powerful spiritual practice that will open your eyes and heart to His boundless miracles.

> **"Be still, and know that I am God."**
> *Psalm 46:10*

CONSIDER IN YOUR
Heart

**In a hustle-happy world, seeking and finding regular
pockets of stillness has the power to change your life from
the inside out.**

---

*How confident are you in hearing and deciphering the voice of God?
What are you willing to sacrifice to increase your sensitivity to His voice?*

*Is His presence a familiar one in your days? How will you look for evidence
of His hand in your life more often?*

Peace

We whisper, beg, and pray.
Peace in the unknown.
Peace in our weakness.
And in the ever-raging storms.

Peace.
To cover our fear,
Confusion,
And worry.

Slowly we learn the
Divine, simple truth:
Peace grows
In our vulnerable patience.

Like the tiny seed
Planted each spring.
We vulnerably believe,
And wait.

Light and water,
day by day—
In tiny amounts,
It miraculously grows.

The warm summer tomato,
Brilliant red,
Sweet like candy,
Our simple reward.

What then,
Of our patience in suffering,
Patience in waiting,
Patience in longing?

Peace.
The brilliant gift given
By the Ultimate Giver
Of all that is good.

In Him,
No wait is too long,
No broken past repair,
No worry in vain.

In Him,
Our peace is deeply rooted,
Patiently grown,
And forever the way through.

Lift up your Heart & Rejoice

Wherefore, lift up thy heart and rejoice, and cleave unto the covenants which thou hast made.

Doctrine and Covenants 25:13

find

DATE   PLACE   TIME

TODAY'S
gratitude

learned ❧ studied ❧ heard

find

....
DATE   PLACE   TIME

TODAY'S
gratitude

learned ⚘ *studied* ⚘ *heard*

find

....
DATE   PLACE   TIME

TODAY'S
gratitude
....

....

....

learned ⬿ *studied* ⬿ *heard*

find

....
DATE   PLACE   TIME

TODAY'S
gratitude

learned ❧ *studied* ❧ *heard*

weekly study . . .

find

....

DATE   PLACE   TIME

TODAY'S
gratitude

learned ❧ studied ❧ heard

Verily I say unto you all: Arise and shine forth, that thy light may be a standard for the nations.

Doctrine and Covenants 115:5

....
DATE   PLACE   TIME

TODAY'S
gratitude

....
....
....

learned ✻ *studied* ✻ *heard*

find

....
DATE   PLACE   TIME

TODAY'S
gratitude

learned ⤙⤚ studied ⤙⤚ heard

find

....
DATE   PLACE   TIME

TODAY'S
gratitude

learned ✦ *studied* ✦ *heard*

. . . .

DATE   PLACE   TIME

TODAY'S
gratitude

learned *studied* *heard*

....

DATE   PLACE   TIME

TODAY'S
gratitude

learned ⊱⊰ *studied* ⊱⊰ *heard*

the LORD GOD has POWER to do all things

Now as to this thing I do not know; but this much I do know, that the Lord God hath power to do all things which are according to his word.

Alma 7:8

find

....
DATE   PLACE   TIME

TODAY'S
gratitude

learned ⚘ *studied* ⚘ *heard*

weekly study...

find

....
DATE   PLACE   TIME

TODAY'S
gratitude

learned ⚘ *studied* ⚘ *heard*

find

. . . .

DATE   PLACE   TIME

TODAY'S
gratitude

learned ↞ *studied* ↞ *heard*

DATE   PLACE   TIME

TODAY'S
gratitude

learned ⊱≪ studied ⊱≪ heard

Be Still

find

....
DATE   PLACE   TIME

TODAY'S
gratitude

learned ✿✿ *studied* ✿✿ *heard*

Look unto me in every thought; doubt not, fear not. Behold the wounds which pierced my side, and also the prints of the nails in my hands and feet; be faithful, keep my commandments, and ye shall inherit the kingdom of heaven. Amen.

Doctrine and Covenants 6:36–37

....
DATE   PLACE   TIME

TODAY'S
gratitude

learned ✤ *studied* ✤ *heard*

Be Still

weekly study . . .

....
DATE   PLACE   TIME

TODAY'S
gratitude
....

....

....

learned ⪼ *studied* ⪼ *heard*

find

....
DATE   PLACE   TIME

TODAY'S
gratitude

learned ❧❧ *studied* ❧❧ *heard*

find

....

DATE   PLACE   TIME

TODAY'S
gratitude

learned ✾ *studied* ✾ *heard*

weekly study . . .

find

....
DATE   PLACE   TIME

TODAY'S
gratitude
....

....

....

learned ✿ *studied* ✿ *heard*

Be
Still

weekly study...

ask in FAITH, believing YOU SHALL Receive

If ye will not harden your hearts, and ask me in faith,
believing that ye shall receive, with diligence in keeping my
commandments, surely these things shall be made known
unto you.

1 Nephi 15:11

....

DATE   PLACE   TIME

TODAY'S *gratitude*

learned ✦ *studied* ✦ *heard*

....

DATE   PLACE   TIME

TODAY'S
gratitude

....

....

....

learned ❧❧ *studied* ❧❧ *heard*

weekly study . . . .

find

....

DATE   PLACE   TIME

TODAY'S
gratitude

....

....

....

learned ✦✦ *studied* ✦✦ *heard*

find

. . . .

DATE   PLACE   TIME

TODAY'S
gratitude

learned ❦≈ *studied* ❦≈ *heard*

Be
Still

weekly study . . .

....
DATE   PLACE   TIME

TODAY'S
gratitude

....
....
....
....

learned ❧❧ *studied* ❧❧ *heard*

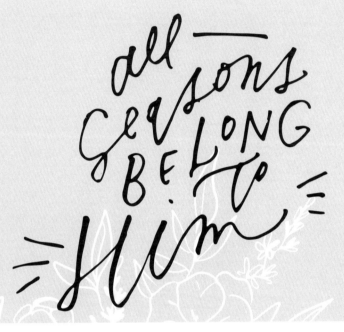

To every thing there is a season, and a time to every
purpose under the heaven.

Ecclesiastes 3:1

find

....

DATE   PLACE   TIME

TODAY'S
gratitude

learned ❧≫ *studied* ❧≫ *heard*

weekly study . . .

DATE · PLACE · TIME

TODAY'S
gratitude

learned ❧—❧ *studied* ❧—❧ *heard*

find

....

DATE   PLACE   TIME

TODAY'S
gratitude

learned ≫⋘ *studied* ≫⋘ *heard*

find

....

DATE   PLACE   TIME

TODAY'S
gratitude ....

....

....

learned ✿✿ *studied* ✿✿ *heard* ————————————

find

....
DATE   PLACE   TIME

TODAY'S
gratitude

learned ⤳ *studied* ⤳ *heard*

LEARN OF ME & LISTEN TO MY WORDS

walk in the meekness OF MY SPIRIT & YOU SHALL find peace in me

Learn of me, and listen to my words; walk in the meekness of my Spirit, and you shall have peace in me.

Doctrine and Covenants 19:23

DATE   PLACE   TIME

TODAY'S
gratitude

learned ❧ *studied* ❧ *heard*

find

....
DATE   PLACE   TIME

TODAY'S
gratitude

learned ⚬≈ studied ⚬≈ heard

find

DATE · PLACE · TIME

TODAY'S
gratitude

learned ✦ *studied* ✦ *heard*

find

TODAY'S
gratitude

learned ❧ studied ❧ heard

weekly study . . .

find

....
DATE   PLACE   TIME

TODAY'S
gratitude

learned ✥ *studied* ✥ *heard*

weekly study . . .

THE LORD is my — SHEPHERD I SHALL NOT WANT.

The Lord is my shepherd; I shall not want.
He maketh me to lie down in green pastures:
he leadeth me beside the still waters.
He restoreth my soul: he leadeth me in the paths of
righteousness for his name's sake.

Psalm 23:1–3

find

DATE   PLACE   TIME

TODAY'S
gratitude

learned ✻ *studied* ✻ *heard*

weekly study . . .

find

....
DATE   PLACE   TIME

TODAY'S
gratitude

learned ❧ *studied* ❧ *heard*

find

. . . .

DATE   PLACE   TIME

TODAY'S
gratitude

learned ❧❧ *studied* ❧❧ *heard*

find

DATE   PLACE   TIME

TODAY'S
gratitude

learned ❧ *studied* ❧ *heard*

find

....
DATE   PLACE   TIME

TODAY'S
gratitude

learned ✤ *studied* ✤ *heard*

Faith is unreasonable

That it is not reasonable that such a being as a Christ shall come; if so, and he be the Son of God, the Father of heaven and of earth, as it has been spoken, why will he not show himself unto us as well?

Helaman 16:18

find

....
DATE · PLACE · TIME

TODAY'S
gratitude

....

....

....

learned ❧ *studied* ❧ *heard*

DATE · PLACE · TIME

TODAY'S
gratitude

learned ❧ *studied* ❧ *heard*

....

DATE   PLACE   TIME

TODAY'S
gratitude

....

....

....

learned ❧❧ *studied* ❧❧ *heard* _____

find

DATE · PLACE · TIME

TODAY'S
gratitude

learned ✦✦ *studied* ✦✦ *heard*

weekly study . . .

Be Still

find

....
DATE   PLACE   TIME

TODAY'S
gratitude

....

....

learned ❧❦❧ *studied* ❧❦❧ *heard*

Be Still

weekly study . . .

you are NEVER ever LOST to Him

But now I go unto the Father, and also to show myself unto the lost tribes of Israel, for they are not lost unto the Father, for he knoweth whither he hath taken them.

3 Nephi 17:4

find

....
DATE   PLACE   TIME

TODAY'S
gratitude

learned ❧⤻ _studied_ ❧⤻ _heard_

find

....
DATE   PLACE   TIME

TODAY'S
gratitude
....

....

....

learned ⋙ _studied_ ⋙ _heard_ ──────────────────

find

....

DATE   PLACE   TIME

TODAY'S
gratitude

learned ⪼⪻ *studied* ⪼⪻ *heard*

find

....

DATE   PLACE   TIME

TODAY'S
gratitude

learned   studied   heard

find

....

DATE   PLACE   TIME

TODAY'S
gratitude

learned ✿❯❯ *studied* ✿❯❯ *heard*

Be Still

KNOW ye NOT THAT ye ARE in THE Hands of God?

Know ye not that ye are in the hands of God?

Mormon 5:23

weekly study . . .

find

. . . .

DATE   PLACE   TIME

TODAY'S
gratitude

learned ❧ *studied* ❧ *heard*

DATE   PLACE   TIME

TODAY'S
gratitude

learned ⤞ *studied* ⤞ *heard*

weekly study . . .

find

. . . .

DATE   PLACE   TIME

TODAY'S
gratitude

learned ⚜ *studied* ⚜ *heard*

DATE..PLACE..TIME

TODADY'S
gratitude

learned ❦ *studied* ❦ *heard*

Be Still

weekly study . . .

··

DATE   PLACE   TIME

TODAY'S
gratitude

learned ✦≪ studied ✦≪ heard

weekly study . . .

NO MATTER WHAT, *there is peace in Christ*

Learn of me, and listen to my words; walk in the meekness of my Spirit, and you shall have peace in me.
I am Jesus Christ; I came by the will of the Father, and I do his will.

Doctrine and Covenants 19:23–24

....
DATE   PLACE   TIME

TODAY'S
gratitude

....

....

....

learned ✦✦ *studied* ✦✦ *heard*

weekly study . . .

find

. . . .

DATE   PLACE   TIME

TODAY'S
gratitude

learned ❧≈ *studied* ❧≈ *heard*

weekly study . . .

....
DATE   PLACE   TIME

TODAY'S
gratitude

learned ✿ studied ✿ heard

weekly study . . . .

find

....

DATE   PLACE   TIME

TODAY'S
gratitude

learned ❧≫ _studied_ ❧≫ _heard_

find

. . . .

DATE   PLACE   TIME

TODAY'S
gratitude

learned 🌿 *studied* 🌿 *heard*

find

....

DATE   PLACE   TIME

TODAY'S
gratitude

learned ❧ *studied* ❧ *heard*

find the GOOD, the JOY,
the heart full of GRATITUDE.

thankful for . . .

thankful for . . .

find the GOOD, the JOY, the heart full of GRATITUDE.

thankful for . . .

thankful for . . .

find the Good, the joy, the heart full of GRATITUDE.

thankful for . . . .

thankful for …

find the Good, the Joy, the heart full of GRATITUDE.

thankful for . . .

find the Good, the JOY, the heart full of GRATITUDE.

thankful for . . . .

thankful for . . .

find the GOOD, the JOY, the heart full of GRATITUDE.

thankful for . . .

thankful for . . .

find the Good, the Joy, the heart full of GRATITUDE.

thankful for . . .

thankful for . . .

WHAT I'M *Learning* *in this* SEASON WITH *GoD*

Reflection

DATE   PLACE   TIME

Even though I feel ...	I still KNOW ...

praying for ....

_____
_____
_____
_____
_____
_____
_____
_____

CHeck in

What I am learning about God:

How this affects the way that I live:

praying for . . . .

Reflection

Even though I feel . . .	I still KNOW . . .

praying for . . .

_____
_____
_____
_____
_____
_____
_____
_____

CHeck in

What I am learning about God:

How this affects the way that I live:

praying for . . . .

Reflection

DATE .... PLACE .... TIME

Even though I feel . . .	I still KNOW . . .

praying for . . .

CHeck in ✦

What I am learning about God:

How this affects the way that I live:

Reflection

Even though I feel . . .	I still KNOW . . .

praying for . . . .

_____
_____
_____
_____
_____
_____
_____
_____
_____

CHeck in

What I am learning about God:

How this affects the way that I live:

praying for . . .

Reflection

DATE · PLACE · TIME

Even though I feel . . .	I still KNOW . . .

praying for . . .

_____

_____

_____

_____

_____

_____

_____

_____

_____

CHeck in

What I am learning about God:

How this affects the way that I live:

praying for . . . .

Reflection

. . . .

DATE   PLACE   TIME

Even though I feel . . .	I still KNOW . . .

praying for . . . .

_____
_____
_____
_____
_____
_____
_____
_____
_____

CHeck in

What I am learning about God:

How this affects the way that I live:

praying for . . . .

Reflection

DATE·· PLACE··· TIME

Even though I feel . . .	I still KNOW . . .

praying for . . . .

_____
_____
_____
_____
_____
_____
_____
_____
_____
_____

CHeck in

What I am learning about God:

How this affects the way that I live:

praying for . . .

Reflection

....
DATE   PLACE   TIME

Even though I feel . . .	I still KNOW . . .

praying for . . . .

_____
_____
_____
_____
_____
_____
_____
_____
_____

CHeck in

What I am learning about God:

How this affects the way that I live:

praying for . . .

Reflection

DATE · PLACE · TIME

Even though I feel . . .	I still KNOW . . .

praying for . . .

_____

_____

_____

_____

_____

_____

_____

_____

_____

_____

CHeck in

What I am learning about God:

How this affects the way that I live:

praying for . . .

Reflection

Even though I feel . . .	I still KNOW . . .

praying for . . .

_____

_____

_____

_____

_____

_____

_____

_____

_____

_____

CHeck in

What I am learning about God:

How this affects the way that I live:

praying for ....

Reflection

Even though I feel . . .	I still KNOW . . .

praying for . . . .

_____

_____

_____

_____

_____

_____

_____

_____

_____

_____

CHecK in

What I am learning about God:

How this affects the way that I live:

praying for . . .

Reflection

DATE   PLACE   TIME

Even though I feel . . .	I still KNOW . . .

praying for . . .

What I am learning about God:

How this affects the way that I live:

praying for . . .

Reflection

DATE .... PLACE .... TIME

Even though I feel . . .	I still KNOW . . .

praying for . . .

CHeck in
What I am learning about God:

How this affects the way that I live:

praying for . . .

Reflection

Even though I feel . . .	I still KNOW . . .

praying for . . .

_____

_____

_____

_____

_____

_____

_____

_____

CHeck in

What I am learning about God:

How this affects the way that I live:

praying for . . . .

ABOUT THE AUTHOR

 Courtney Casper is a wife, mom, writer, hand-letterer, and relentless encourager. She is passionate about linking arms with others as they navigate their own roads toward faith, offering vulnerability and compassion along the way. Bottom line? She wants you to know that **YOU ARE LOVED.**

Instagram: @courtneycasper.letters
Website: courtneycasper.com